GOODNESS

by

Carole MacKenthun, R.S.M.
and Paulinus Dwyer, O.P.

illustrated by Vanessa Filkins

Cover by Vanessa Filkins

Songs by Kathy Jones, Judy Hartwig

Shining Star Publications, Copyright © 1986
A Division of Good Apple, Inc.

ISBN No. 0-86653-363-X

Standardized Subject Code TA ac

Printing No. 98765

Shining Star Publications
A Division of Good Apple, Inc.
Box 299
Carthage, IL 62321-0299

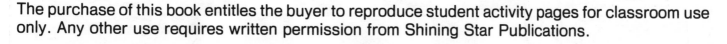

DEDICATION

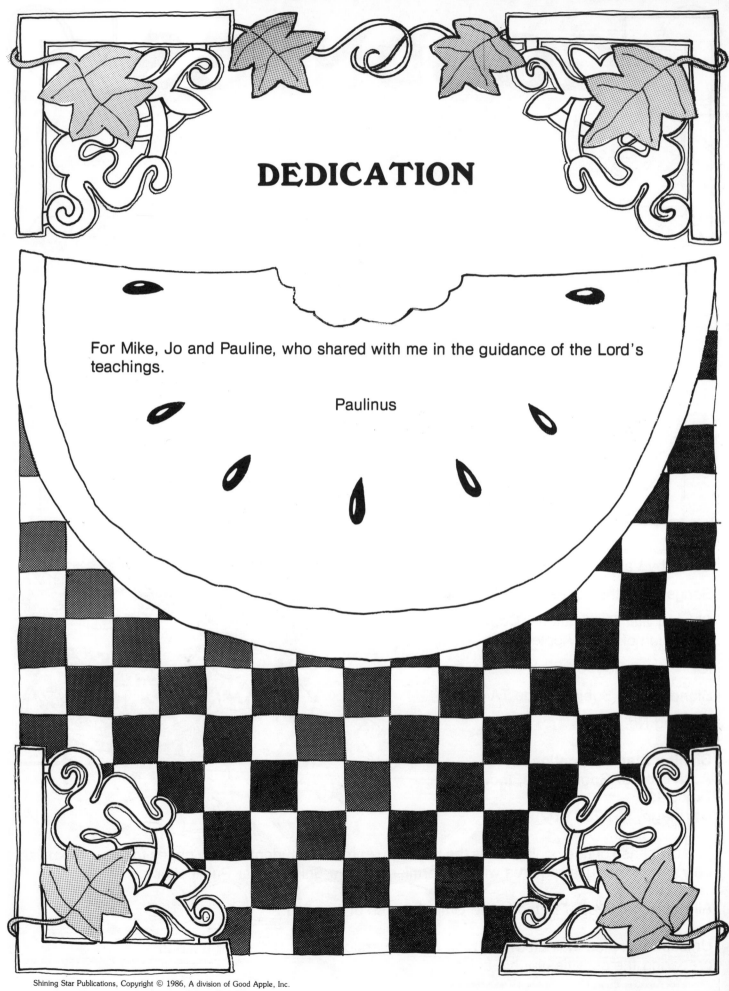

For Mike, Jo and Pauline, who shared with me in the guidance of the Lord's teachings.

Paulinus

INTRODUCTION

"For the fruit of the Spirit is in all goodness . . . ."   Ephesians 5:9

God created the world and saw that it was good. He fashioned us in His own image and likeness and is intimately involved in the very texture of our lives. He revealed to us through Jesus who we are and how we are to live.

Since we have experienced God's goodness, we have the responsibility to share it with others. We do this because it is Jesus' command that if we are to follow Him, we must do so by loving others. He entrusts us with the task of bringing goodness to the world. We must let God's power flow through us to others.

Contained in this book are games, puzzles, songs, work sheets and a variety of ideas that are designed to assist students in developing a better understanding of God's goodness, the goodness in others and the goodness in themselves.

The purpose of this book is to aid educators in teaching children about this treasured fruit of the Spirit, Goodness. These unique activities can be completed either individually or in a group. A Scriptural passage on "goodness" is listed at the top of each idea, and more references are given in the back of the book for reflection or to embellish the activities.

TABLE OF CONTENTS

Shining Star Publications, Copyright © 1986, A division of Good Apple, Inc.

CELEBRATE GOODNESS

"They shall abundantly utter the memory of thy great goodness, and shall sing of thy righteousness."

Psalm 145:7

SPREAD GOOD NEWS

Make a suggestion box for your classroom. Provide paper and pencil near the box. Have the students think of ways to make the world a better place. When they think of something, they should write it on the paper and drop the paper into the suggestion box. At the end of the week, share the suggestions aloud.

Other topics might include:
    How to Spread the Good News
    How to Make Our Classroom Better
    How to Be a Good Friend.

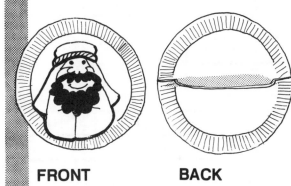

FRONT   **BACK**

Have students select famous biblical characters to research. Each student then writes a short biography of his person and records it on a cassette tape. Next the biblical character is drawn on the back of a large paper plate. Half of another plate is stapled behind it to form a pocket to hold the tape. Finished products can be placed in a special listening center!

Decorate an area in your classroom to look like water around an island. On a piece of paper, write the words "Good News to Share" at the top, and place the rolled paper in a bottle. Students may visit this center, write their good news and read the good news of their classmates.

"But the fruit of the Spirit is . . . goodness . . . ." Galatians 5:22

COMPUTER FUN

Computers use a binary alphabet to read information. Using the following binary code, decipher this saying, which encourages us to be good.

CODE

A	10000	B	01000	C	11000	D	00100	E	10100
F	01100	G	11100	H	00010	I	10010	J	01010
K	11010	L	00110	M	10110	N	01110	O	11110
P	00001	Q	10001	R	01001	S	11001	T	00101
U	10101	V	01101	W	11101	X	00011	Y	10011
				Z	01011				

SAYING

00101	00010	10100

10110	10011	11001	00101	10100	01001	10011

11110	01100

11100	11110	11110	00100	01110	10100	11001	11001

00010	10000	00001	00001	10100	01110	11001

11101	00010	10100	01110

11101	10100

10000	01001	10100

01100	10000	10010	00101	00010	01100	10101	00110

00101	11110

11110	10101	01001	11001	10100	00110	01101	10100	11001

NOW:

Use the binary code given and make a coded message to give your friends to encourage them to be good.

" . . . God loveth a cheerful giver."   II Corinthians 9:7

COMPUTER FUN-2

Using the binary alphabet given on the previous page, decipher this proverb. On a separate sheet of paper, tell what it means to you and how it can help you to grow in goodness.

10011	10100	11001	00101	10100	01001	00100	10000	10011

10010	11001		10000	00110	01001	10100	10000	00100	10011

10000		00100	01001	10100	10000	10110

00101	11110	10110	11110	01001	01001	11110	11101

10010	11001		11110	01110	00110	10011		10000

01101	10010	11001	10010	11110	01110		01000	10101	00101

00101	11110	00100	10000	10011		10010	11001

00101	00010	10100		00110	10010	11100	00010	00101

11110	01100		00110	10010	01100	10100

Use the proverb you deciphered and design a poster for your room or give it to a friend.

"I will lift up mine eyes unto the hills . . . ."

Psalm 121:1

THE EYE OF GOD

Try to make your own "Eye of God" and give it as a gift to someone who has been good to you. Larger ones can be used for display; smaller ones can be worn as necklaces, pins and earrings.

MATERIALS:

Two toothpicks, sticks, dowels, or twigs
Colored yarn or string

PROCEDURE:

1. First tie two sticks together to make a cross by wrapping the yarn several times around in one direction and then several times the other way. Pull yarn very tightly.

2. Next weave one strand of yarn over one stick, under it again, and then around it. Continue this pattern with each stick. Other colors may be added by tying a new string to the previous one.

3. Finally dip the end of the stick in glue and wrap the end of the yarn around it.

SCRIPTURE SUNDAES

HOW TO MAKE THE SUNDAES:

Glue one circle on the top back of sundae. Now glue the other circle on the back of the first one, but put the glue only on the top half. This makes a "lip" to hang the topping on the top of the ice cream.

Glue
Don't glue

White paper

Zacchaeus

I climbed a tree to see Jesus and He asked to dine with me. This changed my life.

back view
of
sundae →

Luke 19:2-8

Jesus touched people with His love and encouraged their goodness to shine forth. This activity familiarizes the students with these biblical characters.

Directions:
1. Use patterns on the following page to make the parts of the sundaes.
2. Write facts about biblical characters on the "ice cream" portion of the sundaes.
3. Scriptural passages can be written on the back of the sundaes in case the students have trouble identifying the characters.
4. The names of the characters are written on the "topping" of the sundaes.
5. Students are to match the topping with the ice cream and then put completed sundaes in the container.

Plastic sundae container

PATTERNS

Ice Cream

Topping

Cherry

"And to godliness brotherly kindness; and to brotherly kindness charity."
II Peter 1:7

A WIND SOCK PROJECT

PURPOSE:
Create a wind sock which celebrates God's goodness to you or which encourages you to strive for goodness.

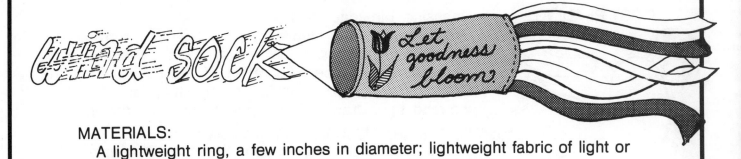

MATERIALS:
A lightweight ring, a few inches in diameter; lightweight fabric of light or bright solid color; scissors and thread; permanent markers

DIRECTIONS:
1. Measure the circumference of the ring.
2. Cut a piece of fabric about 1 inch wider than the circumference.
3. Cut the fabric at least 2½ times longer than width.
4. Make a design on the fabric. Use permanent markers, appliqué, stitchery, etc.
5. Stitch the edges of the fabric together to make a tube shape.
6. Hem the top of the tube over the ring. Keep the edges of fabric on the inside.
7. Attach "tails" to the bottom hem, if desired. Sock is open on the bottom end.
8. Attach string to sock ring to suspend.

  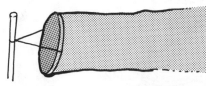

Here are some mottoes to choose from for your wind sock.

Carry God to your world.
Let goodness bloom.
Put your hand into the hand of God.
God keeps His promises.
Color your life with goodness.

Learn to do good.
Rise above the ordinary.
I will never forget you.
Be kind to one another.

If you can dream goodness, you can become it.
He makes all things new.
The flower fades, but the word of God stands forever.
Made in heaven, serving with love.
No road is long with a friend at your side.

" . . . the earth is full of the goodness of the Lord." Psalm 33:5

PRAYER CELEBRATION

HYMN: He's Got the Whole World in His Hands

OPENING PRAYER: God, our Father, you are great indeed. Your goodness is found in all of Your creation. Thank You for these wonderful gifts. May we continue to find You in the beautiful things of Your world.

FIRST READING: Genesis 1 (an adaptation)
(Read the following meditatively. Pause after each stanza. Soft instrumental music may be played in the background. A suggestion would be "Adoration of the Earth" from the *Grand Canyon Suite* by Grofe. Students may listen quietly to the reading or draw their interpretations on art paper.)

In the beginning everything was very dark.
    The Spirit of God moved upon the face of the waters . . .

Then God made the heavens and earth.
    He saw that it was good . . .

God said, "Let there be both light and darkness."
    He called the light the day
    And the darkness He called night . . .

God made the land and water.
    He called the land Earth.
    And the water He called the sea . . .

He said, "Let plants and fruit trees grow up from the land."
    God saw that it was good . . .

Then He made two great lights, the sun and the moon.
    He also made the stars which twinkle in the heavens . . .

God filled the water with whales and living creatures,
    And He brought forth birds and let them fly . . .

He made every kind of living creature—beasts, cattle, little creeping things . . .

God created man and woman in His own image.
    He blessed them and gave them the earth as their home . . .

Then He looked upon everything that He created and knew it was good . . .

SILENT MEDITATION: Let us ponder in silence the wondrous beauty and wealth of variety in God's creation . . .

CLOSING PRAYER: O Heavenly Creator, You take such good care of the birds, flowers and everything in the world. May we always remember that You have even greater love for us. Amen.

"Wherefore also we pray always for you, that our God would count you worthy of this calling, and fulfil all the good pleasure of his goodness . . . ." II Thessalonians 1:11

THE THINGS JESUS TAUGHT US

Words and Music
by
Kathy Jones

CHILDREN'S PRAYER

Words and Music
by
Judy Hartwig

Je-sus lis-ten to my prayer, Keep me al-ways in your care. Let my words and

ac-tions be beau-ti-ful to thee. And dear Sav-ior as I grow, Your sal-va-tion

let me know. Bless my family, Bless my neigh-bors with your love.

"Oh that men would praise the Lord for his goodness, and for his wonderful works to the children . . . ."   Psalm 107:8

SPECIAL GIFTS

" . . . make thyself a glorious name."   Isaiah 63:14

In the message below, each letter stands for the letter that comes after it in ABC order. (Example: C = D and Z = A) Decode the passage and you will have a prayer of thanks for the special gifts God has given you.

NG   FNC,   LX   FNC!   GNV   FQDZS   XNT   ZQD.   VGZS

___   ___   ___   ___!   ___   ___   ___   ___.   ___

ZL   H   SGZS   XNT   RGNTKC   SGHMJ   NE   LD?   XNT

___   _   ___   ___   ___   ___   __   ___?   ___

FZUD   LD   RODBHZK   FHESR;   XNT   LZCD   LD   Z

___   __   ___   ___;   ___   ___   __   _

KHSSKD   KDRR   SGZM   ZM   ZMFDK;   XNT   BQNVMDC

___   ___   ___   __   ___;   ___   ___

LD   VHSG   GNMNQ   ZMC   FKNQX.

__   ___   ___   ___   ___.

Read Psalm 8 and see how David sang his song of thanksgiving.

THE GOODNESS OF OTHERS

''And I myself also am persuaded of you, my brethren, that ye also are full of goodness . . . .''
Romans 15:14

Search through the newspaper and find an article that tells about a person who did a good deed for someone else. Write about the article in the space provided.

THE GOOD NEWSPAPER

_____
Title of News Article

_____
Author

Summary of Story:

_____

_____

_____

_____

_____

_____

_____

_____

_____

"This is a faithful saying, and these things I will that thou affirm constantly, that they which have believed in God might be careful to maintain good works. These things are good and profitable unto men."   Titus 3:8

GOOD WORKER AWARD CLUB

This award will assist teachers in affirming children who have been seen helping others. Encourage children to create their own awards for those who have been helpful to them. When they take these home, parents will know that "good deeds" are alive in the classroom.

Good Worker Award Club

TO: _____

FOR: _____

FROM: _____

"For the fruit of the Spirit is in all goodness and righteousness . . . ."

Ephesians 5:9

STUDENT SILHOUETTES

Make silhouettes of each member of the class. Have each student stand between a strong light (such as one from an overhead projector or filmstrip projector) and a piece of light-colored paper which is taped to the chalkboard. Trace the shadow with a pencil. Cut out the silhouette and glue it on a piece of dark paper. Each classmate is then invited to write a good quality about this student on his silhouette. Hang the finished silhouettes on the bulletin board or another special place in the classroom. Everyday select a different silhouette and discuss the goodness in each student.

" . . . the goodness of God endureth continually." Psalm 52:1

LOOK

Name	Act of Goodness

Because God made us, His goodness is shown through us and those who are close to us: our parents and families, our classmates and teachers, our neighbors and those with whom we play. In the scroll at the right, make a list of those with whom you associate, and during the next day or week, look for something particularly good that each person does. Write it next to his name.

Make a similar list for several more days or a week. When you say your prayers at night, thank God for the goodness that He is sharing with you through other people.

"But the path of the just is as the shining light, that shineth more and more unto the perfect day."
                                                                    Proverbs 4:18

A BRIGHT IDEA

Write a thank-you note to someone who has been good to you. Let this person
know how your life was brightened by her act of kindness.

GOD'S GOODNESS

"Oh how great is thy goodness . . . ." Psalm 31:19

TV COMMERCIAL

Think of all the TV commercials that you have seen this past week. Catchy tunes and clever words help to make a successful commercial.

Write a TV commercial to advertise the goodness of God. You can use a familiar tune or make one up on your own! Here is an example:

GOD . . .
He brings good things to living!
He brings good things to life!

_____

_____

_____

_____

_____

Illustrate your commercial inside the TV screen.

MODEL OF GOODNESS

START

Apostles leave in boat.

Storm comes up.

Peter becomes afraid and sinks.

Jesus appears.

Peter jumps on water.

Jesus helps Peter into boat.

Jesus saves Peter.

Jesus reaches out hand.

PEACE AND JOY

FINISH

God's goodness was shown in a very special way when Jesus helped so many who were hurting. Read in Matthew 14:22-32 about one of the times when Jesus helped Peter. Then as you work your way through the maze, think about how often Jesus helps you when you ask, even if the problem, like Peter's, is of your own making.

"I am the good shepherd, and know my sheep, and am known of mine." John 10:14

PURPOSE: This bulletin board familiarizes the students with the Scriptural story of the good shepherd found in the Gospel of John.

PROCEDURE: 1. Read John 10:11-19 to the students. Compare Jesus to the good shepherd. For example:

   a. The good shepherd gives his life for the sheep.
      Jesus gave His life for us on the cross.

   b. The good shepherd helps the sheep find food.
      Jesus gives us His body and blood to strengthen us.

   c. The good shepherd watches and cares for his sheep so that no wolves or other harm comes to them.
      Jesus protects and cares for us and leads us away from evil.

   d. The good shepherd leads the sheep on the right path to green pastures.
      Jesus is Our Way and leads us to everlasting life.

   e. The good shepherd unites his sheep and brings them into one fold.
      Jesus unites us as one family in His Church.

2. Give each child a sheep. (Pattern is provided on page 24.) Each child writes his name on the sheep.

3. Sheep are added to the bulletin board.

VARIATIONS: 1. Write Scripture verses or references about the good shepherd on the sheep.

Suggested verses:

      Psalms 23:1, 100:3
      Isaiah 40:11
      Ezekiel 34:11-17
      Matthew 18:11-14
      John 10:27, 21:16
      Hebrews 13:20
      I Peter 1:18-19
      Revelation 7:17, 17:14

2. Have children write on the sheep their own suggestions for being good shepherds, for example, helping an elderly person across the street, aiding a little child who is lost, etc.

EXTENDED ACTIVITIES: 1. Draw a large sheep on poster board. Tape the sheep to your chalkboard. Print the following on the sheep: "I Am Lost." Have children write about things they have lost, sign their names, and attach their notes to the sheep using paper clips. Another idea would be to have the lost items placed near the poster so that they can be claimed quickly.

2. Teach the song "Feed My Lambs," p.25.

SHEEP PATTERN

FEED MY LAMBS

John 21:15-17

Words and Music
by
Kathy Jones

"...they ... delighted themselves in thy great goodness."   Nehemiah 9:25

SUNCATCHER

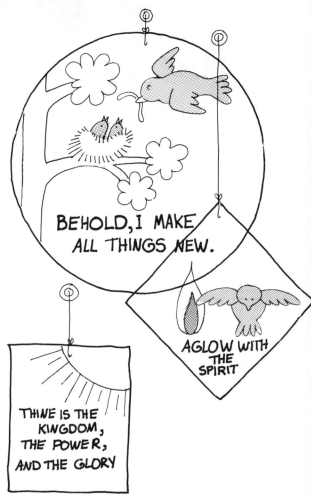

God's goodness is all about us: in our parents and families, in our classmates, in the beauty of the world. Make a suncatcher to hang in your window to remind you each morning to celebrate God's goodness.

MATERIALS: Clear plastic (overhead transparencies or the like), colored markers, yarn.

DIRECTIONS:
1. Cut two circles of clear plastic 4 inches in diameter or two squares 4 inches on a side.
2. Print a motto on one piece of the plastic using a permanent marker.
3. Decorate the motto.
4. Cover the finished design with the other piece of plastic.
5. Secure the edges with colored plastic tape or sew them together with yarn.
6. Use a piece of yarn to hang it in your window.

MOTTOES:
You can use one of these mottoes or you may wish to find one of your own.
1. Seek first the kingdom of God and His justice.   Matt. 6:33
2. Behold, I make all things new.   Rev. 21:5
3. Lord, that I may see.
4. I will be his God and he shall be my child.   Rev. 21:7
5. I am Alpha and Omega, the first and the last.   Rev. 21:6
6. Thine is the kingdom, the power, and the glory.
7. Made in heaven; serving with love.
8. Christ has died; Christ is risen; Christ will come again.
9. Because I love you.
10. Aglow with the Spirit.
11. I will uphold you with the right hand of My justice.   Is. 41:10
12. I have called you by name; you are mine.   Is. 43:1
13. I will never forget you.
14. I've got the Spirit.

". . . and my people shall be satisfied with my goodness, saith the Lord."

Jeremiah 31:14

THE GOODNESS OF GOD

Draw an appropriate picture in each box to illustrate the verse from Psalm 23.

PSALM 23 (an adaptation)

The Lord is my shepherd. There is nothing I shall want.	**He makes me lie down in green pastures.**	**He leads me beside still waters.**
He brings peace to my soul.	**He leads me in the right path.**	**If I walk through a dark valley, I will not fear.**
He is with me.	**He prepares a table before me.**	**Goodness will follow me all the days of my life.**

"Behold therefore the goodness . . . of God. . . ."   Romans 11:22

JESUS HELPS US BE GOOD

Jesus loved to tell stories. When people asked Him questions about how to be good, He would explain by telling a story. Many of these stories are listed below. Read each story in your Bible. Then rearrange the letters to find the title of the story. Use the letters in the squares and answer the question at the bottom.

1. C O O I L T N S   Luke 15:8-10

__ __ __ __ __ □ __ __

2. A D D E E M R S S T U   Mark 4:30-32

__ __ __ __ __ __ __ __ □ __ __ __

3. E E H L O P S S T   Matthew 18:11-14

__ __ __ __ □ __ __ __ __

4. O N O S S T W   Matthew 21:28-32

__ __ __ __ □ __ __ __

5. A E L N S T T   Matthew 25:14-30

__ __ __ □ __ __ __

6. E O R S W   Mark 4:2-9

__ __ __ __ __

7. A E E L N V   Luke 13:20-22

__ __ __ __ __ __

8. R A E G S I A T T T   Luke 13:22-29

__ __ __ __ __ __ □ __ __ __

9. A C H I M N R   Luke 16:19-31

__ □ __ __ __ __ __

10. O O D G   A A A I M N R S T   Luke 10:25-37

__ __ __ □ __ __ __ __ __ __ __ __ __

11. C D E I K W   A B D H M N N S U A   Luke 20:9-17

__ __ __ □ __ __ __ __ __ __ __ __ __ __

□ __ __

QUESTION: What do these stories lead to?

__ __ __ __   __ __ __ __ __ __ __

"For how great is his goodness . . . ." Zechariah 9:17

GOOD NEWS

Sometimes cheerleaders use megaphones to make their voices louder. In the megaphone below, write your own cheer about the goodness of Jesus. Then shout out this Good News to everyone!

ROUNDUPS

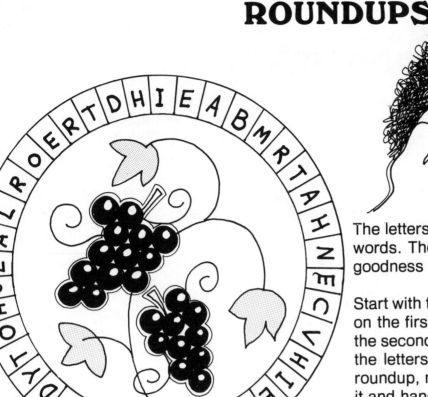

The letters in this circle are really a chain of words. They will help you remember God's goodness to you.

Start with the **I** at the top of the wheel. Print **I** on the first line. Skip a letter and print **A** on the second line. Continue in this way until all the letters are used up. Then cut out your roundup, mount it on heavy paper, decorate it and hang it in your room.

''____ ____ ____ ____ ____

____ ____ ____ ____ ____ ____

____ ____ ____ ____ ____ ____ ____ ,''

____ ____ ____ ____ ____ ____ .

QUOTATIONS

Make a roundup wheel for each member of your family. Give the wheels at dinner and explain that each wheel contains a message that will help everyone have a happy day.

You may use some of the quotations at the right on your roundups, or you may wish to find some of your own which will more appropriately fit the members of your family. The Book of Proverbs and Psalms are good places to look.

1. ''Your word is a lamp to my feet and a light for my path.'' Psalm 119:105 (NIV)
2. ''I delight to do thy will, O my God: yea, thy law is within my heart.''   Psalm 40:8
3. ''O sing unto the Lord a new song: sing unto the Lord, all the earth.'' Psalm 96:1
4. ''And they that be wise shall shine as the brightness of the firmament . . . .'' Daniel 12:3
5. ''The mouth of the righteous speaketh wisdom . . . . The law of his God is in his heart . . . .''   Psalm 37:30, 31
6. '' . . . whoever practices and teaches these commands will be called great in the kingdom of heaven.'' Matthew 5:19 (NIV)
7. ''. . . If a man love me, he will keep my words: and my Father will love him . . . .'' John 14:23

"And he spake many things unto them in parables . . . ."   Matthew 13:3

PARABLES

Through parables, Jesus taught us how to live a life of goodness. Each parable gives a lesson through a story. Some of these stories are listed below. Read each story in your Bible and then unscramble the letters to find the title. Then place the numbered letters on the appropriate blanks to answer the question found below.

1. J N S T U U A D E R S T W   Luke 16:1-14

_ _ _ _ _ _ _ _ _ _ _ _ _ _
                                    1

2. A A E G I M R R A E F S T   Matthew 22:1-15

_ _ _ _ _ _ _ _ _ _ _ _ _
  14   2

3. O O D G D E E H H P R S   John 10:1-21

_ _ _ _ _ _ _ _ _ _ _ _ _
   8   13

4. A B E N R R G F I E R T E   Matthew 21:18-23

_ _ _ _ _ _ _ _ _ _ _ _ _
  7

5. N E T S G I I N R V   Matthew 25:1-13

_ _ _ _ _ _ _ _ _ _
               6

6. C H I R O L F O   Luke 12:16-21

_ _ _ _ _ _ _ _
  11

7. A D G I L R P O N O S   Luke 15:11-32

_ _ _ _ _ _ _ _ _ _ _
   5   12

8. E N T   Matthew 13:47-50

_ _ _
   10

9. S U U N T J D E G J U   Luke 18:2-8

_ _ _ _ _ _ _ _ _ _ _
                  9

10. A L C D N E   Mark 4:21-24

_ _ _ _ _ _
     3

11. A E L P R   Matthew 13:45-46

_ _ _ _ _
      4

QUESTION: What happens when we study these stories?

_ _ _ _ _ _ _ _ _ _ _ _ _ _ _ _ _ _.
1 2 3 2 4 5 6   4 7 8 9 10 1 11 12 13 8 14

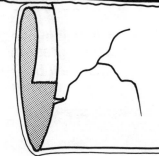
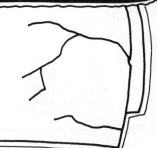

"... the kindness and love of God our Saviour toward man appeared." Titus 3:4

CONSIDER THE LILIES

Rearrange the letters in this acrostic so that each word describes God's care for us. As you decipher each word, read the reference in the Bible to see how this tells about God's love. When you finish, there is a special word about God's feeling toward us in the squares down the center.

DTOMOFCRE	___ ___ ___ ☐ ___ ___ ___ ___	Isaiah 52:9
RSTUT	___ ☐ ___ ___ ___	Proverbs 3:5
FLICMUER	___ ___ ___ ☐ ___ ___ ___	Genesis 19:16, 17
VOEL	___ ___ ___ ☐	Jeremiah 31:3
SENDOGOS	___ ___ ___ ☐ ___ ___ ___ ___	Psalm 107:8
SKIENDNS	___ ___ ___ ___ ☐ ___ ___ ___	Psalm 117:2
SJUT	___ ___ ☐ ___	Deut. 32:4
UTRTH	___ ___ ___ ☐ ___	Psalm 96:13
RIIVGGFON	___ ___ ___ ___ ☐ ___ ___ ___ ___	Num. 14:18
PLEH	___ ___ ☐ ___	Isaiah 41:10

Write the special word on this line. _____

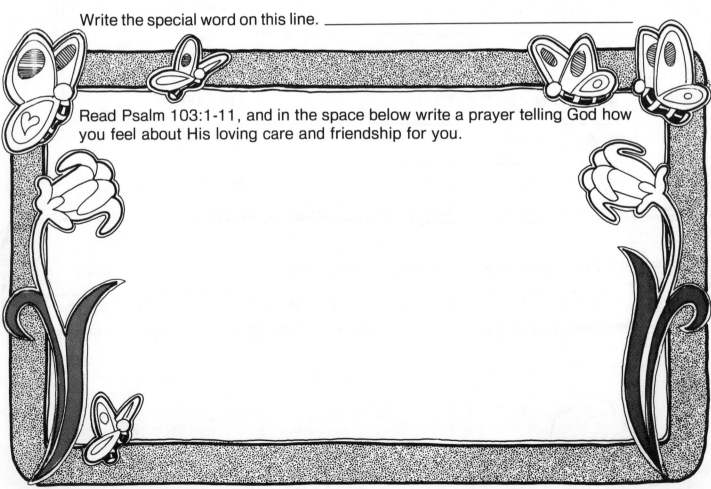

Read Psalm 103:1-11, and in the space below write a prayer telling God how you feel about His loving care and friendship for you.

GOD DELIVERED ELIJAH

'' . . . see the goodness of the Lord . . . .''   Psalm 27:13

The Bible is filled with stories of God's GOODNESS. He delivered many people in strange and wonderful ways. Below is a story of how God delivered Elijah. The story is written in rebus. Can you discover the meaning of these pictures and words? Write the story below the pictures. Check your work by reading I Kings 17:3, 4.

"G + [dove] – J   3 – R   [hen] + CE,

& T + [thimble] – CH   3 – R   EAST + WARD,

& H + [eye] + D   TH + [eye] + SELF   B + [knife] – T

THE BR + [hook] – H   CHERITH,   T + [hat]

IS   [fly] + 4   JORDAN.   & [hand] – M

SHALL   [fly],   T + [hat]   THOU SHALT

DR + [inkwell with quill] OF THE   BR + [hook] – H;   & [eye]

HAVE   CO + [stick figure walking] + DED   THE   RAVENS   2

[feet] – T + D   3 – R   TH + [ear] – A + E.

BONUS: Find another story of deliverance in the Bible. Use another sheet of paper to write the story in rebus.

Shining Star Publications, Copyright © 1986, A division of Good Apple, Inc.

I AM GOOD

I KNOW MY BIBLE

'' . . . the blessings of goodness . . . .''   Psalm 21:3

It is good to know how to find things in your Bible quickly. This game will give you some practice using your Bible. Search the Scriptures to find a person, book of the Bible, place, plant, verb and animal that begins with the letters in the top boxes. For example, the top, left-hand square must be completed with the name of a biblical person beginning with the letter S. Give a Scripture verse for each answer. How many squares can you complete in 30 minutes?

	S	C	R	I	P	T	U	R	E
person					Paul Acts 27:43			Free	
book			Free		Book of Titus	Free			
place			Free						
plant				Free			Free	Free	Free
verb	Seek Matthew 7:7		Free						Envy I Cor. 13:4
animal				Free		Free		Free	

"Put on therefore, as the elect of God, holy and beloved . . . kindness . . . ."
Colossians 3:12

FOR THE FAMILY

Goodness at home helps make a happy family. Doing small things because we love each other makes family life easier. Maybe just a smile . . . maybe just picking up your clothes or someone else's . . . maybe just thoughtfulness at the table. Small things—these are the things that count! Continual sharing with each other makes family life strong.

In each box write the name of one member of your family. Then draw a picture in the box of one **small** thing you can do for that person.

If you need more boxes, draw them on the back or on a separate sheet of paper.

NAME

NAME

NAME

NAME

SOMETHING GOOD

Show your goodness to your family by doing something which is fun for them to share. Have a "mini-party" and make one of these recipes to serve. Call it a "Just Because I Love You" party.

POPCORN BALLS

MATERIALS:
¼ pound (1 stick) margarine
1 package (10 oz., 30-40) regular marsh-mallows
6 cups popped popcorn

Melt the margarine in a large saucepan over low heat. Add marshmallows a few at a time and stir gently until completely melted.

Continue heating and stirring 2-3 minutes. Stir in popped popcorn. Mix well. Allow the popcorn to cool until it can be handled.

Spread a little margarine on the palms of your hands and form the popcorn into balls. Place on waxed paper until completely cooled. Makes about 20 balls.

MICROWAVE FUDGE

MATERIALS:
1 pound powdered sugar (1 box)
½ cup cocoa
¼ cup milk
¼ pound (1 stick) margarine

Stir cocoa and powdered sugar together until well mixed. Put into a microwave-safe pan. (An 8" x 6" Pyrex cake pan is ideal.) Put ¼ cup milk over the mixture. Lay ¼ pound margarine on top. Cook on high in the microwave for 2 minutes. Remove and stir just to mix. Put in freezer for 20 minutes. Cut into pieces. Can be kept in refrigerator until used. Makes 30-40 pieces.

"But let us, who are of the day, be sober, putting on the breastplate of faith and love; and for an helmet, the hope of salvation."   I Thessalonians 5:8

COAT OF ARMS

A coat of arms is a special kind of advertisement. It is a symbol that stands for a person or a family. Often it suggests important events in a person's life or a family's history.

Design a personal coat of arms for yourself. Some names suggest a picture idea. For instance, Florence means Flower of God and Christopher means Christ bearer. Look up the meaning of your name and use the symbol somewhere. Show some event in your life when something good you did or someone did for you was very important. Perhaps you had an answer to prayer which seemed miraculous.

A coat of arms is often divided into two, three, or four parts. Each part should have a different symbol. When you are finished, hang your coat of arms with others in your group for a display.

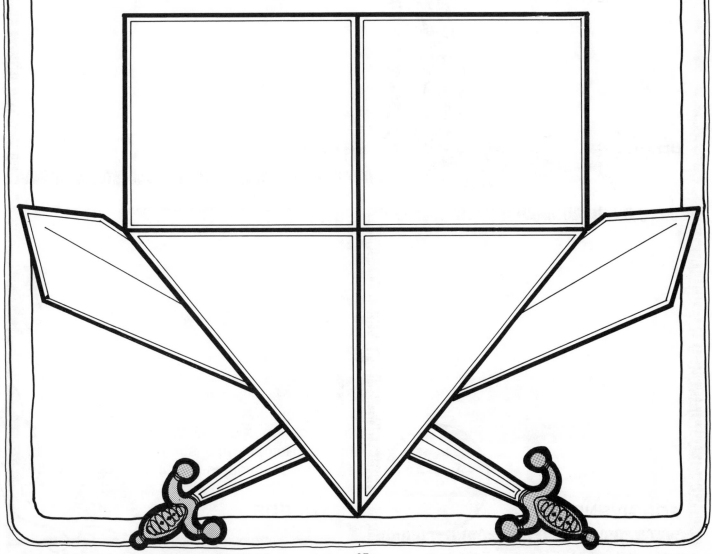

"Pray without ceasing."   I Thessalonians 5:17

PRAYER

We grow in goodness as we talk to God in prayer. How do we pray? There are many ways. We compliment God for being so great, for making beautiful flowers, birds, the sun, a lovely day. We say thank you for some things He gives us when we ask, or we tell Him we are sorry for something mean we did. We tell Him our needs and beg His help.

In each box write one of these prayers to God.

PRAISE

THANKS

FORGIVENESS

NEEDS

GOODNESS MAZE

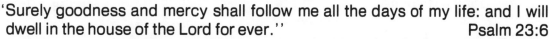

''Surely goodness and mercy shall follow me all the days of my life: and I will dwell in the house of the Lord for ever.''   Psalm 23:6

Goodness can be defined as those qualities and virtues which make us what God wants us to be. The words in this game help us think of God's goodness to us and our goodness as we imitate Him.

See how many words you can find in this maze. As you look for the words, think how these increase your understanding of goodness. Letters may go up, down, forward, backwards or even twist. The same letter may be used more than once, but you must follow a line between each letter. Two can play. Keep lists of the words you find. The one who finds the greatest number of words wins.

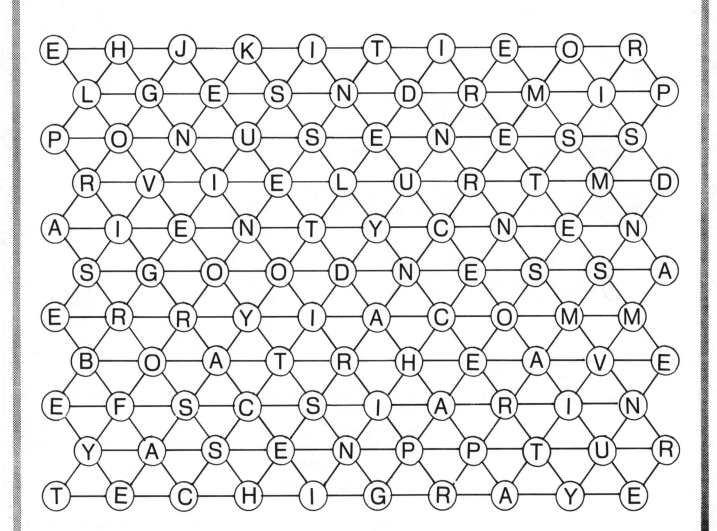

Here are some of the words in the maze:

charity	commandments	Christ	forgiveness	gentleness	giving
goodness	teaching	grace	happiness	help	heaven
Jesus	kindness	love	merit	mercy	obey
praise	prayer	promise	sorry	true	virtue

GIFTS OF GOODNESS

"... Inasmuch as ye have done it unto one of the least of these my brethren, ye have done it unto me."

Matthew 25:40

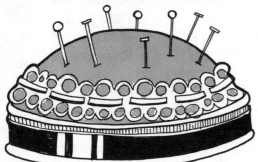

Jesus tells us that whatever we do for others, we do for Him. Read the story that Jesus tells about the King of Heaven in Matthew 25:31-40. It is easy to do good works for loved ones. It is not so easy to do good works for a stranger. Below are two craft ideas you can make and take to a nursing home or hospital to cheer up a shut-in. Make one and take it today!

PIN CUSHION

MATERIALS:
narrow-mouth canning lid and ring
6" x 6" piece of fabric
scraps of lace and ribbon
half a styrofoam ball (2½" diameter)
glue, scissors

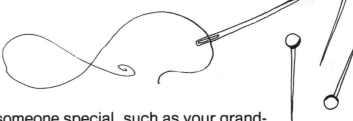

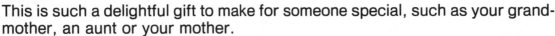

This is such a delightful gift to make for someone special, such as your grandmother, an aunt or your mother.

Set the canning lid, rubber side down, in the canning ring. Glue the fabric on the styrofoam, and then glue the fabric-covered styrofoam in the ring making a pin cushion.

Decorate the ring and the edge of the pin cushion with lace and ribbon. Stick straight pins and needles into your pin cushion. Now it is ready for that special someone to use for all those sewing projects.

ROCK PAINTING

MATERIALS:
clean rocks
acrylic paints
black felt pen
varnish (optional)
felt, glue, newspapers

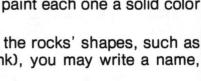

Place clean rocks on a layer of newspapers, and paint each one a solid color with acrylic paints or model paints.

When rocks are dry, paint designs suggested by the rocks' shapes, such as flowers, etc. With a black felt pen (permanent ink), you may write a name, message or Bible verse on each rock.

You might want to put a coat of varnish on your rocks and glue felt on the bottoms of the rocks.

Use your rocks for paperweights, party invitations, or to decorate windowsills.

Shining Star Publications, Copyright © 1986, A division of Good Apple, Inc.

"... Christ forgave you, so also do ye." Colossians 3:13

PROBLEMS OF FORGIVING

Choose one of the letters below and pretend you are an advice columnist. Answer the letter on a separate sheet of paper. If you have time, answer the other two letters also.

Dear Rachel,
I feel terrible. First I hit my sister. When my mother scolded me, I yelled back at her. Then my father called to me and I screamed, "You'll never see me again." I was going to run away, but I didn't. Instead I hid. The whole family is mad at me. Now I really feel sad and lonely. Tell me something to do to make up with them.

Juan

"Forbearing one another, and forgiving one another, if any man have a quarrel against any: even as Christ forgave you, so also do ye." Colossians 3:13

Dear Rachel,
Jimmy lives next door to me. He doesn't play ball very well. The other children don't want him to play on their team, and he was hurt when I didn't choose him. Now he stays in his house all the time. I think he just watches TV. I don't know what to do about it. What should I do?

Your Friend,
Dillon

Dear Rachel,
The other girls purposely make fun of Courtney because she always has the nicest clothes. Once when the other girls were there, I would not speak to her. So now she is hurt and we used to be best friends. I am sorry I did it. What should I do to make it up to her? Please help me.

Anne

"... I will be gracious, and will show mercy ...."   Exodus 33:19

MAY I HELP?

We are friends to many people. We love them because God is their Father and because they are good. To be good friends we do what we can for them, helping them when they need us.

In his letter, James tells his friends about helping. Read what he has to say in James 2:14-18. Then fill in the chart below to tell how you would show your friendship for God and those near to you.

NEED	WHAT I WOULD DO	HOW I WOULD DO IT
An elderly person is lonely.		
The baby is crying.		
A playmate is hurt.		
Mother is cooking.		
A classmate can't do a math problem.		

"And he said, I will make all my goodness pass before thee . . . ." Exodus 33:19

HELP FILL NOAH'S ARK

Learning to be "good" can be very difficult for children. Changing behavior takes patience and love. Rewarding positive change is one way to help children replace negative behavior with positive behavior.

One idea is to begin by telling the students the story of Noah. Emphasize that Noah obeyed God, even when the task seemed to be an unusual one and all his peers laughed at him. After reading the story of Noah, play this activity to start new positive patterns in your classroom.

Draw or paint a large ark on a bulletin board. You may wish to use this pattern for your ark. Cut many copies of the animal awards found on the following pages. Use different colors; construction paper works well.

During the day give animal awards to each student for particular positive behaviors. The specific behaviors should be fully understood by all participants at the beginning of the day. One day you may wish to establish the following game rule: Each time a student says "please" or "thank you," he receives an animal award. A second day you may wish to give each student five animals. A student must give back to you an animal each time negative behavior is shown (verbal and non-verbal). At the end of the day, all animals in possession of a student can be attached to the ark. The student can write his name on the animals before he attaches them to the ark. In all activities the student must be aware of his behavior, and, of equal importance, he must work collectively with the other students to achieve a goal.

The reward for filling the ark could be a class field trip, extra recess or a similar surprise. At the end of the project, the students should be encouraged to take their awards home to share with parents and family.

SPLENDID

ILLUSTRIOUS

NAME _____

SUPERB

FOR _____

TO _____

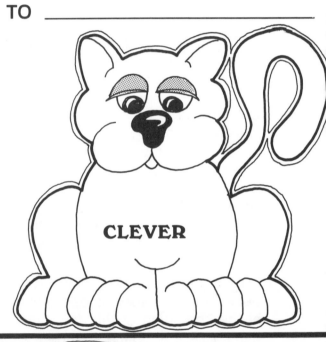

CLEVER

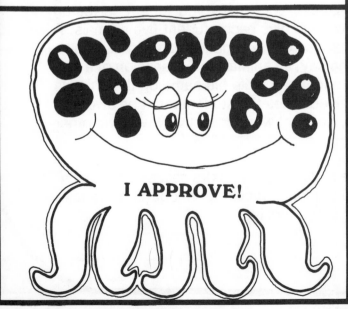

I APPROVE!

TER RR RR IFIC

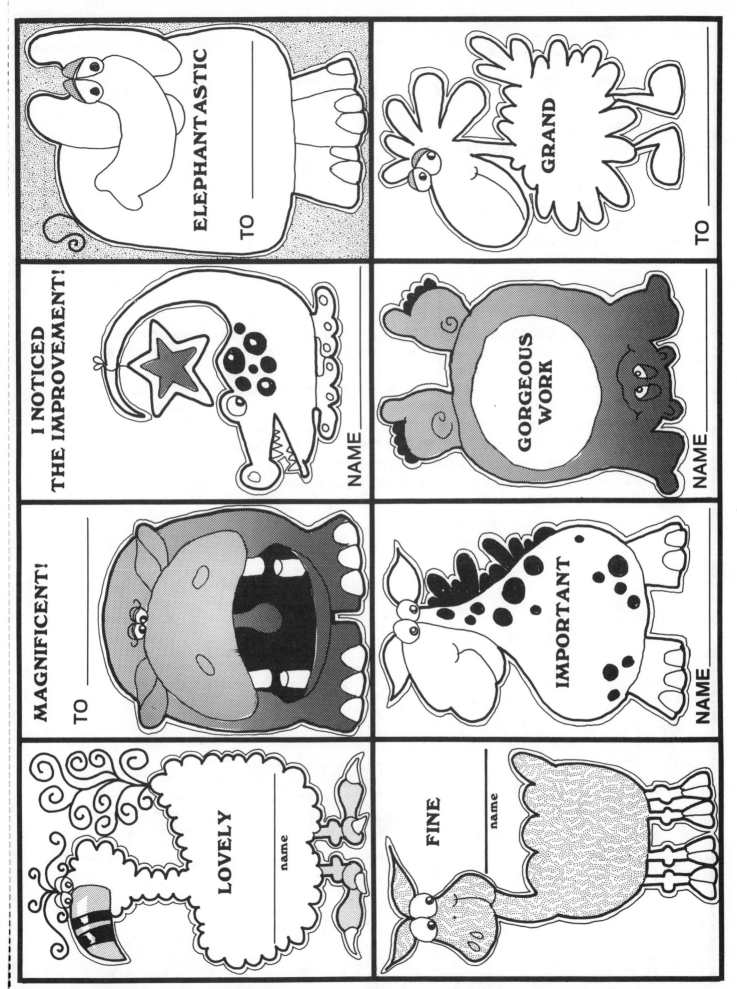

ELEPHANTASTIC
TO ____

GRAND
TO ____

I NOTICED
THE IMPROVEMENT!
NAME ____

GORGEOUS WORK
NAME ____

MAGNIFICENT!
TO ____

IMPORTANT
NAME ____

LOVELY
name ____

FINE
name ____

Here is a GOOD recipe to try!

ROSIE'S CHOCOLATE BROWNIES

INGREDIENTS:

2 squares (2 ounces) melted
   unsweetened chocolate
1 cup sugar
2 tablespoons butter
1 egg
1 teaspoon vanilla
1 cup sifted flour

1 teaspoon baking powder
½ cup undiluted Carnation Evaporated
   Milk
1 cup chopped nuts

PROCEDURE:

1. Preheat the oven to 350º F.
2. Put the chocolate in the oven in a heat-proof dish and allow it to melt.
3. Put the sugar, butter, egg and vanilla into a medium-sized bowl. Mix with a wooden spoon until well-blended. Add melted chocolate.
4. Pour flour into a sifter and sift it gently before measuring out 1 cup. Stir the sifted flour with baking powder.
5. Stir half the flour mixture into the butter. Add the Carnation Evaporated Milk.
6. Stir the batter until smooth. Add the rest of the flour and chopped nuts. Mix the batter until lumps have disappeared.
7. Pour the batter into a buttered 9″ square pan. Bake about 30 minutes.

ANSWER KEY

COMPUTER FUN p. 6

The mystery of goodness happens when we are faithful to ourselves.

COMPUTER FUN-2 p. 7

Yesterday is already a dream;
Tomorrow is only a vision;
But today is the light of life.

SPECIAL GIFTS p. 15

Oh God, my God! How great you are. What am I that you should think of me? You gave me special gifts; you made me a little less than an angel; you crowned me with honor and glory.

JESUS HELPS US BE GOOD p. 28

1. Lost coin
2. Mustard seed
3. Lost sheep
4. Two sons
5. Talents
6. Sower
7. Leaven
8. Strait Gate
9. Rich man
10. Good Samaritan
11. Wicked husbandman

ANSWER: His Kingdom

ROUNDUPS p. 30

'' I am the vine and you are the branches,'' said the Lord.

PARABLES p. 31

1. Unjust steward
2. Marriage feast
3. Good shepherd
4. Barren fig tree
5. Ten virgins
6. Rich fool
7. Prodigal son
8. Net
9. Unjust judge
10. Lamp
11. Pearl

ANSWER: We learn about wisdom.

CONSIDER THE LILIES p. 32

comforted
trust
merciful
love
goodness
kindness
just
truth
forgiving
help

SPECIAL WORD: Friendship

SCRIPTURAL PASSAGES ON GOODNESS

Exodus	33:19; 34:6
Numbers	10:32
Judges	8:35
II Samuel	7:28
I Kings	8:66
I Chronicles	17:26
II Chronicles	6:41; 7:10; 35:26; 32:32
Nehemiah	9:25; 9:35
Psalms	16:2; 21:3; 23:6; 25:7; 27:13; 31:19; 33:5; 52:1; 65:4; 65:11; 68:10; 107:8; 145:7
Proverbs	20:6
Isaiah	63:7
Jeremiah	2:7; 31:12; 31:14; 33:9
Hosea	3:5; 10:1
Zechariah	9:17
Romans	2:4; 11:22; 15:14
Galatians	5:22
Ephesians	5:9
II Thessalonians	1:11